¿Quién ha visto mi orinal?

Mij Kelly

y Mary McQuillan

Título original: *Have you seen my potty?*
Publicado originalmente por Hodder Children's Books, 2007
© del texto, Mij Kelly 2007
© de las ilustraciones, Mary McQuillan, 2007
© de la traducción Belén Cabal, 2008

© de esta edición, RBA Libros, S.A., 2009
Pérez Galdós, 36 08012 Barcelona
www.rbalibros.com / rba-libros@rba.es

Primera edición: febrero 2009
Compaginación: Editor Service, S.L.

Impreso en China

Referencia: SLHE082
ISBN: 9788498673166

¿Quién ha visto mi orinal?

ESCRITO POR

MIJ KELLY

ILUSTRADO POR

MARY McQuillan

SerreS

Esta es la historia de Maribel, que tiene algo muy **importante** que hacer, algo **importante** que hace cada día…

...hasta que un día fatal...

...alguien le quitó el orinal.

¡Qué fastidio! ¡Qué dolor!
¿Dónde pongo ahora el culito para
hacer popó?

¡Sólo un pillo descarado,
granuja y malvado puede
robar a alguien el orinal
cuando lo tiene preparado!

—Mirad lo que he encontrado en el suelo tirado.

—¿Es un casco, un puchero?

—No. ¡Es un cacatiesto!

—¿Has visto mi orinal?,
—le preguntó a la vaca.
Pero la muy gorda
se hizo la sorda.

—He perdido mi orinal
y si no lo encuentro
pronto,
esto
puede acabar
mal...

—No tengo ni idea de lo
que es un **orinal**?
—dijo el animal.

—Que se dé prisa
la vaca,
que se nos
sale
la caca.

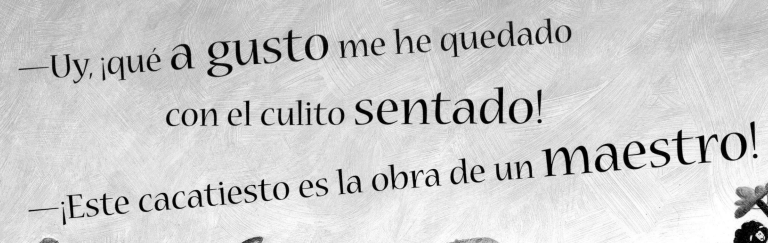

—Uy, ¡qué **a gusto** me he quedado
con el culito **sentado**!

—¡Este cacatiesto es la obra de un **maestro**!

Oh, qué desastre para la pobre Maribel, que tiene algo muy **importante** que hacer.

—¿Has visto mi orinal?, —le preguntó
al caballo, que dijo sin sobresalto:
—Ahora estoy muy ocupado.
Vuelve y me lo preguntas
cuando haya terminado.

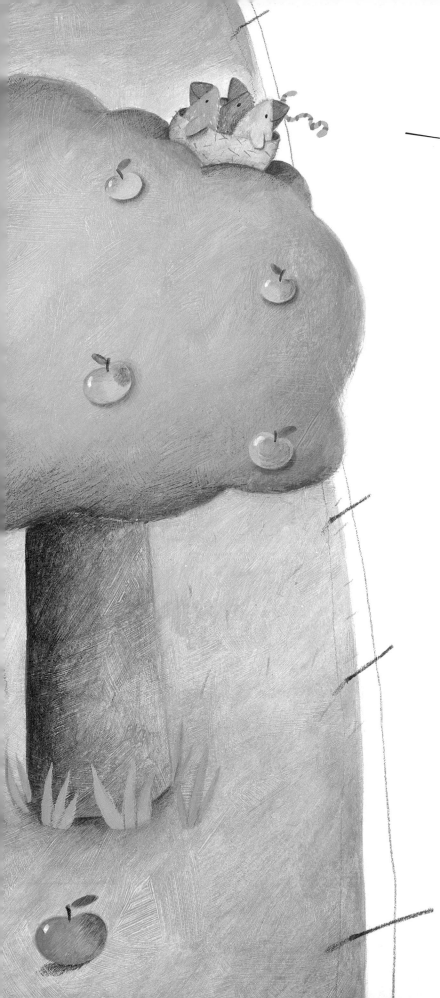

—¿Qué es un orinal?

—Date prisa, esto empieza a olerme mal.

—Me estoy haciendo pis.

Oh, qué desastre para la pobre Maribel, que tiene algo **muy** *importante* que hacer.

—¿Has visto mi orinal?, —le preguntó a la oveja, que estaba sentada en un pequeño asiento color teja.

La oveja quería ayudar.
Intentó ser amable.
Pero esa palabra, «orinal»,
¿qué podía significar?

—¿A Maribel qué le pasa?

—A mí no me lo preguntes.

—¡Yo quiero hacer caca!

—¡Qué **fascinante** invento!

—¡Qué **maravilloso** elemento!

—Un poco de **privacidad** es siempre de **desear**.

Oh, qué desastre para la pobre
Maribel, que tiene algo

muy importante que hacer.

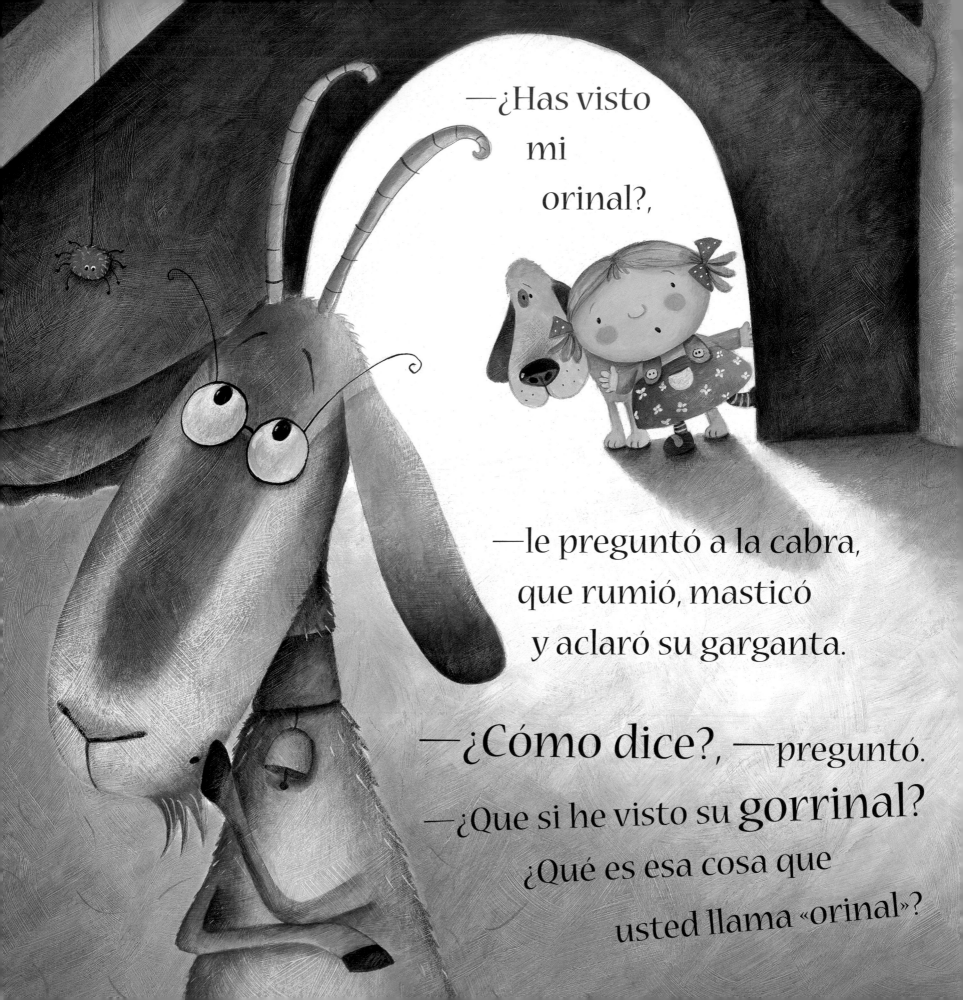

—¿Has visto
mi
orinal?,

—le preguntó a la cabra,
que rumió, masticó
y aclaró su garganta.

—¿Cómo dice?, —preguntó.
—¿Que si he visto su gorrinal?
¿Qué es esa cosa que
usted llama «orinal»?

—¡Es cómodo!
—¡Es limpio!

—Desde que llegó a la granja, ya sólo huele a naranja.

Oh, qué desastre para la pobre Maribel,
que tiene algo muy **importante** que hacer…

Ella es muy **puntual** cuando
tiene que sentarse en su **orinal**.

Si no lo encuentra ya…
lo hará en **cualquier lugar**…

—Tenemos
lo que
necesitas.

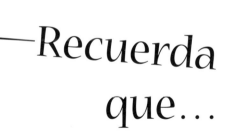

—Recuerda
que…
si tienes ganitas…
…¡utiliza un cacatiesto
de sillita!

Esta ha sido la historia de Maribel, que tenía algo muy **importante** que hacer.

Penumbra

Cover painting: "Coral Sea" by Claribel Cone.

Book & cover design by Lisa Rappoport.

Printed at All-American Printing, Petaluma, California on Strathmore 100% cotton soft white 80# text paper (30% recycled, carbon neutral, made using 100% wind power).

ISBN: 978-0-9889694-4-5

Longship Press is an independent publishing company based in San Rafael, California. The managing editor is Lawrence Tjernell. The website is www.longshippress.com.

Penumbra

Lisa Rappoport

LONGSHIP PRESS :: SAN RAFAEL :: 2019

Contents

Sail Away

STONE EGG

I asked
how her chicken
had died and
she said It became
eggbound
and I thought
of the awful
suffering
of that one
particular
chicken
and in the same
breath of all our
eggs, germs,
spermatozoa,
unsprouted seeds,
that which should
be born and is not,
that which kills
us with its
un-birth, which
solidifies within
us, which is what
she said happens
to the egg, and
wondered what
if anything
we can do
next time.

A Grammar of Loss

"Death is a black camel, which kneels at the gates of all."
—Abd al-Qadir, Algerian military & political leader and poet, 1807-1883

I. USE OF THE PAST TENSE
It is surprisingly difficult
to begin to use the simple past
(never simple) or past perfect
(far from): like the quickly-
corrected stumbles we make
in a foreign tongue,
embarrassing ourselves; but here
not only grammar but heart
resists, yearning for the present
progressive, the continued present,
the present of ongoing action
which leads to the future.

II. SYNONYM
When the friend has gone,
we tend to say, "She has passed,"
"He has gone on," "Dearly departed,"
"We have lost him," avoiding
the straightforward reference
to death.

III. CASE
In some languages each noun
possesses a case, such as ablative
or genitive, and in this case the case
would be accusative; but whom
to accuse?

IV. NUMBER
The verb and the noun
must conform, like to like;
but what is the correct number
of loss?

V. DANGLING PARTICIPLE
Leaving so much hanging, those who
still live, the conversations which seem
to continue, the unasked and unanswered
questions . . .

VI. DIAGRAMMED SENTENCES

I | have lost | you
forever

You | are \ lost
to me   forever

VII. CONJUNCTION
Conjunctions show relationship.
What has been joined
may then be sundered.

VIII. SUBJUNCTIVE MODE
Use of the subjunctive expresses
an idea as desirable, supposable,
conditional: Would that she were alive.
If only it were to turn out differently.
I wish she were here with us.

IX. INDEFINITE RELATIVE PRONOUN
Whatever happened had to happen.
Whichever treatment she sought
was inadequate. Whoever could
have believed it would end
like this?

for Leila
7/26/62–10/8/09

ONE WEEK

The backs of dahlias: green
stems bled into petals of flat white.
Remembered fireflies, covered mirrors,
heat lightning. My mother's hair
in a box.
The mute empty clothes. Drawers
we never opened. Sun on the carpet.

ASHES OF ROSES

It's raining here; the roses are heavy
on their thorned branches
bending toward the grass. My father,
the phoenix, lies down in his ashes,
breathes with difficulty, rises. His nest,
asbestos and tar, never scorches. His wife's
unclaimed ashes rest in an urn in a room
full of others. My father breathed fire
for forty years; his ruined lungs won't heal.
Some people know why they are here, why
they stay. He lives to live, I think — it's what
he's always done. His house is sold, the flowers
he planted gone, his one love dead;
even his bitterness begins to fade.
No rain can drench his smoldering will,
his death-grip on life. He lives to prove he can.
Whatever grace there is for dying men
may come to him in time. If there is time.

THE CALLING DOOR

My father said goodbye to his nurse and oxygen; curled
on his side, he removed the cannula, the kind nurse told me.
Beyond, the door stood wide, calling Why not?
as he lay in his bed. My dark heart bled to know

that after he removed the cannula, as the kind nurse told me,
he had to bide another while, two whole days more,
lying in his bed. My dark heart bleeds to know
his pain. I cried, despite the absence of surprise.

He had to bide another while, two whole days more.
I see him smaller than he possibly could be;
I cry for his pain, despite the absence of surprise,
imagine an ancient shriveled homunculus

smaller than he possibly could be,
between bleached sheets. For some the passage out,
imagining an ancient shriveled homunculus,
is over-narrow; for fear they won't glide by

between bleached sheets on their passage out
from here to there, they dwindle, as if on purpose.
Their hearts are over-narrow; for fear they won't glide by
they shrink en route to death; before they go out

from here to there, they dwindle, as if on purpose,
and say goodbye to us and oxygen. They lie curled
and shrunken en route to death. Before others should go out
they see the door stands wide, calling and calling *Why not?*

What Remains

for M.N.

Tenderly once again I place them in
the bark I fashioned of smoke and hope, and nudge
it toward the current's pull with my heel,
recite the Kaddish and pray my desperate plea
for these people, these dead parents, these
specters who haunt me to please embark and leave
what remains of my damaged soul
to me; to please be quiet now, be still.
This rite is interrupted by the recall
of a long-departed date: the cold of a fall
night on the water, the ceremonial
burial at sea of his dead
parakeet. And though he cared enough
to craft a ritual, to fill the little
floating casket with tobacco and
suchlike gifts for the afterlife,
and though as he pushed the feathered corpse away
from our canoe he spoke of missing the bird,
I knew his own neglect was what had killed
it: Too many hungry days, the damp chill
of the houseboat when he forgot to pay
the electric bill, the failure even to find
it a warmer home. And still I placed my heart,
that sadly atrophied muscle, in his hands
where the future unfolded as it always will.
Yes, he was, let's face it, crazy, or
if not, he was three doors away; and possibly

so were they, the pair whose non-corporeal
remains I try to sell down the river;
and yes, most likely so am I, or else
why do I build these inadequate vessels
and why tell you about it? It's their voices
I need to kill.

Narrow Escape

I used to recount to myself
the close calls: those early excursions
after a hard day in kindergarten, clambering
up giant concrete blocks to the railway trestle,
where I would lie supine along the track
as the train roared beside me, never
brave enough to flatten myself between the rails;
the nail tree I couldn't always find
in the woods, but when I did,
as a matter of honor, I had to climb
the iron spikes, distanced for a man's legspan,
not a young girl's; and later the serious
exits—the dive from the cab of the speeding
pickup truck; the car I glissaded
off the wet curving road into a ditch; the tall
ladder that collapsed and left me sprawled
across a window frame; the long seconds clinging
to a bar beneath the rising chair lift until I made myself
jump; the filly who tried to kick me to death;
the rearing geldings I dashed between
as they pawed shod hooves at each other—
I could go on. Lately I view these as blood-red herrings,
distractions from the real near-deaths:
the ones I don't see coming,
don't know about, so many more,
so much more constant, so infinitely
close that I am almost
afraid to go to sleep.

Autopsy

I imagine the coroner's gloved
hands on my body, touching where no hand
has been for so long, understanding
what no one has known. All is made
clear: fractures old and healed, recent
pain, daily trouble. Naked in death, shame
too has died. What is there to fear?
My body tells its tale where there is
only one to hear. And I, I who know
much but not all, who despite everything
would like to wait for the end of the story,
where have I gone now it is over?

Sic Transit

—the way on buses or trains,
not long-distance routes but
local transportation systems, faces
are gilded, sometimes by the light
(and perhaps there is something
in the glass not used in most
windows?) but often it seems
simply because we are in transit,
expectant and ungrounded, able
to receive and emit illumination
by some not usually possible means,
which for how many years
I've noticed and pondered
but never till now set pen
to page to mention —

ODE TO THE SEMICOLON

Above
the line a
floating dot,
hovering
over the

half-
drowned
comma,
curved—
or is it
in fetal
position?
Curled
finger
which
beckons;
or signals
a pause
(longer
or more
serious
than we
might
other-
wise
make):
more
of a
cae
sur
a

.

Vanishing Away: Regretting Hopkins

Shook foil is done for, along with pied beauty,
azure, and every type of sprung rhythm.
God is dead, as well as his or her
grandeur. The language has dwindled, as have
its users. Now we're rich in disses,
in cruel jabs to the fearful heart.
What could save us has been swept under
the carpet, there to fester, lusterless,
beside the dust and little disarticulated
mouse vertebrae. Together in the dark
the dirt, the bones, and the burnished gold
will mingle till their spangled moment comes again.

RE: EDWARD HOPPER

In Paris, he realized that he had fallen in love with light.
"The Writer's Almanac," July 22, 2014

What a stellar choice of love object: one
which will always abide, or at least for part
of each day (except in winter above the Arctic
Circle); will never reject you, unless blindness
strikes; will accept your devotions with equanimity.
Accompanies your thoughts and meanderings
without complaint or judgment. Seems to warm
you. Cannot mislead with false appearances, since
what is it but appearance? Contains multitudes,
being both wave and particle. Is steadfast
other than during the odd eclipse. Lingers, increases,
fades, shifts, thus maintaining fascination. Never turns
a corner. Touches not your heart, except
metaphorically, and therefore breaks it not.
Gilds the surface. Remains there.

THE VOYAGE

And God made him die during the course of a hundred years and then He revived
him and said: "How long have you been here?" "A day, or part of a day," he replied.
—The Koran, II 261 [quoted in Jorge Luis Borges's "The Secret Miracle"]

This frail vessel deludes us daily
into thinking a few ribs, a fragile carapace,
a brittle endoskeleton can suffice
to protect the enclosed organs: the self that is a clock
beating time until the end of time. Embarked
on our coracle, awash without oars,
the journey lasts as long as
any single lifespan—insect
years, dog years, tortoise years. A minute
lingers into infinity, a decade speeds
by. If time is what keeps everything
from happening at once, life must be
the anteroom of death, the fleeting
moment in which the butterfly
dreams it is a human. An instant
enfolds the event horizon, a particle
and a wave walk into a bar, a dog walks
out of a bar on its hind legs, not well
but at all: and no one is surprised,
and it isn't the dog that died
but the breath and the mind
and the cosmos we either create
or inhabit, the gift or the burden,
the theory or the reality of relativity.

NAVIGATION

A moment of a garden
is what you told me, a moment
of flowered green air perched
above the bay, clinging in tiers onto
the steep incline. Now boats move below,
heartbeats on the moving water, lights, means
of arrival or of escape. From here all falls away,
rushing down in the night. What tentative ligatures
clasp us to this earth. We navigate with radar,
faith, heat-seeking devices. Make lives
where fate deposits us. Keep the fires burning.

Ships bear lanterns to signal their whereabouts: approaching,
you know their bulk lies to the right of red, to the left
of green. Floating homes, moored or unmoored, skimming
the thin membrane of separation. So much remains
below water: barnacles, slowly widening cracks,
sunken memories. A sailor trusts in buoyancy. On land
gravity is salvation. There are only two shores:
The lamp we light in the dark morning,
the other lamp we light at dusk.

Here Be Dragons

COFFEE CAKE

Cream 1/8 lb. butter, 1 cup sugar
(or less if history's undertow tugs
you toward salt, toward bitterness).
Add 2 whole eggs, 1 1/2 cups flour, sifted
with powdery memories of your mother's kitchen,
entire, fragmented, smashed, a mishmash of love,
regret, cracked hope, nourishment bestowed
and withheld, acrid white dust. Leaven with
1 1/2 tsp. baking powder, for levity, even
chemically induced; for ease,
whatever is light, what rises, what floats.

What is a mother's recipe without
milk, 3/4 cup, life's beginning, always shadowed
by the nuance of turning, the possibility of souring.
One tsp. vanilla or maple flavoring —
the ersatz favored above the genuine: was that
to pinch pennies or because it lasted when the real
thing, what my parents thought real, didn't
persist, fermented perhaps, drunk on its own
sweetness? Can any pleasure, any promise,
endure? Better not to risk wrecking
on the shoals of what might not be sure.

Decades later, awash in my own hesitations,
I ask: Why not blueberries? Fresh or frozen,
summer or winter, that untamed blue. The topping:
Mix nuts, cinnamon, sugar, sprinkle well over batter before *baking.*
To everything an order, a natural harmony, do this and that

must follow; keep safe by circumscribing
life. Can we stop death from taking
its turn?

My mother tells us what must be done:
Bake 20-30 minutes in oblong pan at 350 degrees.
That "oblong" catches my eye, the beauty
of the word in her slanted handwriting, the slight
unexpectedness of the choice among others more
expected, those elongated consonants, the second
"o" practically a diphthong, the feel of the sounds
in my mouth like our rounded ancestral Russian,
diasporal Yiddish, the syllables of Jews on the run
yet conversing, keeping the mother tongues
alive, streaming off ships to congregate
in the kitchens of the New World and partake
in the ritual breaking of the bread,
tasting the salt, the coffee, the cake.

RESURRECTION

The four hands of my mother and her mother kept working, busy
with needlepoint, sewing, knitting, darning, gardening, busiest
in the kitchen, where how long it might take to prepare
a dish didn't matter. No one grudged the time, the trip to the fish store
for the whitefish, the pike, the oily carp which would be transformed,
given new identity, boned and skinned and fed into the grinder clamped
onto the edge of the kitchen table, its long silver arm
turning steadily, its open snout swallowing all, even the scorn
for others who bought their gefülte fish in jars, the shared
scorn. Fish skins and bones simmered with onions
in the cast aluminum pot. My mother and my grandmother talked
over the grinding and chopping, using enough Yiddish to warn
me I wasn't welcome, discussing what now will never be known.
Their words floated into the steaming broth. Chickens arrived
with their feet still attached. Stray pin feathers were singed off
in the flame of the gas burner. Each part had its assigned use,
the liver, the back, the neck. They concocted defiant delicacies
from what those better-off disdained — the stringy,
neglected neck gnawed with delight, the tail, the jellied
feet, the secret pouches of tenderness called oysters scooped
from the bony back. Soup was made from carcasses, cooking
oil rendered from fat; our teeth rendered pleasures and virtues
from thriftiness, from necessity. My mother didn't teach me
to cook. She cooked, she cleaned, she washed dishes alone
with her thoughts or with her own mother. We weren't close
enough, or she was guarding her only territory, or my lack
of inclination was too much for either of us to overcome.

I wanted to be in a tree. I wanted to be on a horse or in the water
or in a book, or most of all in a different life, but now I want
to have been there in the kitchen with them, I wish I had taken
part, I wish their resourcefulness had found some use
for me, for even what was unappetizing about me,
awkward, unfamiliar, hard to love, easy to discard.

Arc

Hospital stays framed the two ends
of her married life. Her bulk was at its least
those times and climbed a bell curve of mass
in between. During her engagement she was
so happy she walked on air. Air failed her,
and she plummeted down the subway stairs
and lay six weeks in a white bed, to rise
slimmer than ever before and wed
my father. So thrilled, she said, to be
wanted, to find a man who would
have her. Convinced, then and forever,
that love lay beyond her horizon,
an undeserved gift, she was doomed
to lifelong gratitude, to visions
of love vanishing into thin air,
someone else's air. She didn't claim
what was hers; the shame of size muzzled
any unvoiced protests. At last cancer
stole her flesh and laid her
diminished body down on those white
sheets, in a room where my father
sat silent, mourning, still full as a stone
well of his unbelieved-in love.

BENEATH THE ARMS

My female forbears have enormous limbs,
legs like a chubby baby with folds at the thigh
and knees dimpled in fat. From their upper arms
depend peninsulas, soft drapey-skinned swellings,
loose and wobbly, trembling at each movement
like butterflies at rest.
All this they detest,
along with other body parts:
wrong hairs, excess girth, pores
too large, scarred skin, ankles
spilling over shoes, ears that won't
lie flat against the head: not
feminine, not seemly, unattractive. They attack
such betrayals with tweezers, diets, doctors,
electrolysis, water pills, vitriol.

I'm sure I'll wake one day to find
my own two arm sacs beside me in bed,
new companions to this earthly life.
Those women never mucked a stall,
mixed cement, plastered walls, hauled
bricks or straw, made hay. They
didn't lift a cast-iron chase of lead type
from stone to printing press, and back,
again and again throughout the day. They
ironed, cleaned, sewed, cooked,
mothered, made art, but still the flesh found its home.
My unseemly occupations may not save me,
my destiny may mock the visits to the gym,

the bicycled miles, the boats paddled,
horses' stalls mucked out and their long sides
groomed; all I ask is, dear
genetic fate, let it be a little longer
until we meet; let me wake a while unaccompanied
before it's too late.

AN EXCESS OF FIREFLIES

My mother liked to drink iced coffee
on humid New Jersey afternoons. This was long
ago, before we feared caffeine or were spooked
by the outcome of so much negligence and downright
abuse of this physical world, before we had reached the point
where anything you ate or drank or breathed might
kill you, as easily as not. Because they were ignorant,
people back then could drink coffee at all hours
without it keeping them up at night.
Maybe if they tossed and turned
they had some other explanation, like
how elusive sleep can be after a thunderstorm,
or the way an excess of fireflies
foretells a night of lying awake.

She would never make fresh coffee for her cold drink;
she only had it if some remained from the morning.
I loved the color, the soft milky brown in the dimpled
amber tumbler, cubes of ice bobbing in their murky sea.
I never learned to like the taste, or to pretend I did.

In warm weather I often have an iced mocha, the bitter
coffee masked by sweet chocolate, the color just as I remember
and my own icebergs cloistered in a narrow glass. It's not humid
here, rarely even very hot; still, far from there in time and space,
I feel the heaviness of that moist summer air, the increased gravity,
the beaded sweat on me and on the glass, the closeness, the distance.

My Cousin and I Chat about Old Times

When my cousin said to me *the catastrophe*
that was your childhood I laughed, taking pleasure
in the phrase, feeling the relief of another's hyperbole,
the sick melodramatic flair: An observer would know,
without even scraping away the decades of dark grime
laid on by hands and contaminants not mine,
that beneath must lie a landscape, painted en plein air,
its original colors lively and untarnished by time;
gazing into which one could nearly
smell the violets by the stream,
feel the breeze shift up and down
the rotund hills in their infinite greens,
hear the dry rustle of leaves
as trees nodded, shivered, nodded again.

CLARION

When I was in the third grade we were told
to choose the band instrument we would
play the following year. I chose trumpet.
Its tone seemed so pure, so attenuated,
as if a voice could speak without subterfuge,
cleanly. My mother said no. It would deform
my mouth, she said, and no boy would ever
want to kiss me. So I downgraded
to clarinet. I was indifferent to it
then, but later on I came to love
its clouded overtones, its soulfulness,
the way it haunts the air like human song.
Was it that denied purity
which turned me from the simple and true?
Now an excess of subtext suffocates
the text; I make myself crazy construing
silence and decoding what was never
encoded. I still want that belled golden metal
to pierce straight to my well-defended heart.

BODY AND SOUL

Like any poor fool in a Russian novel,
I yearned to live that grand love that ennobles
petty existence. It wasn't the Irishman so jealous
he begrudged my sojourns with books; not
the artist who disregarded my poems; never
those who knew not my heart, because I saw
into theirs in time to guard my own. No, I wanted
it all: soul to soul; hearts entwined; carnal delights.
I retch to think how little I learned, and at what
cost. All that reading did not a thing
to educate me in the art of self-preservation.
Didn't the heroines go for broke? And broken
is what they got. The heroes mostly survived
and lived to love once more. (When fiction
intrudes on life, reject fiction.)

An idiot has brains enough to feel shame.
A heart that breaks can always break again.

EATING CHOCOLATE CAKE WITH THE LIGHTS OFF

—as if what I put in my mouth is the night, its rich
bittersweetness, thin sweeter dusting of powdered
Milky Way meandering across the domed vault,
each feature detectable without magnification, and my chewing
takes in the silence of space which is not really silent,
and makes me think of Krishna's mother
looking into his mouth and seeing the whole universe.

And this dark stillness I've taken into me descends into my own
inner dark which will remain unillumined unless medicine
decides to go there, and as I remain mainly ignorant I see
no reason not to imagine stars there as well, the constellations
of my body, the Northern Dessert, the Little
Anxiety, the Greater Anxiety, Lisa's Belt, watching unmoved
over the unceasing movements
of my world.

HOW TO MAKE A MANGO PURSE

for Sasha when she was four

First get a mango. Eat it. After slicing
away what comes easily, rip the innermost
flesh from the pit with your teeth. Let juice
run down your chin. When you're satiated,
set the pit on a sill in the sun to dry.
Its surface will be scored with the marks
of the knife. Speculate on scars,
skins, coverings, what is hidden or
revealed. As the drying days pass
the stone will split.
                Scraped
heart, you should have been an onion.
Rivulets of tears have dampened your
chambers. It's time to come apart.

THE SPACE BETWEEN

Sasha, at thirteen, likes to talk on the phone
with her girlfriends. She says sometimes
they don't say anything, they stay silent for minutes
and listen: to breath, to static, to the hum
and mutter of distant conversations.
They hear what's there and what isn't.
They're breathing in the space between child
and woman, what's already happened
and what might never be, trying hard
to unravel codes sent by those
a little farther down the road. They don't
have to learn how to be; they even can
be together, quietly, without chatter, two
or three at a time. Their wings
don't work yet, the feathers are too damp,
the pinion muscles weak and reluctant.
The changelings are stuck here with us.
They don't know how the crow flies, they only
know walking on the ground is used up.
These girls are too old now for the play
they once spun for hours, whole days,
minds wheeling all over the map
and above. Now their play is mute,
but connected. How rich such silence,
and how rare. I'm hoping this girl
won't forget looking back. I'm hoping
she'll forget only enough to become light,
able to lift off the earth, but remembering
to circle from time to time, to come home.

Fauna

INVASION

Leave one remnant of sweetness unguarded
and they're there. Not swarming at first,
just a few moving with beautiful randomness.
Before you know it the trail has been blazed,
the scouts have led the troops to the fort,
they've stormed it and captured their desire
and long after any perceptible spoils of war
remain to devour, they stay. Ants, tribute to
negligence, warning to be more vigilant,
companions of the spaces we rashly claim as ours:
You visit my home more than anyone, trample
my defenses, share what I prefer to keep to myself.
You now, the worms later.

WHEN IS THE RIGHT MOMENT TO TELL YOUR THERAPIST HER FLOOR IS CRAWLING WITH ANTS?

While I was not talking, not knowing where to look and staring at the floor, I noticed the carpet was alive with ants, seething in the clay-colored fibers. Clever and devious, they froze when I focused directly on them, but thanks to excellent peripheral vision I could check out their prodigious activity undetected. Oh ants, angst, atoms, angströms. Initially I thought I was hallucinating; and after a few minutes I thought so too. Later on the ants seemed like some dreck I had dredged up and dragged onto the doorstep, wagging my tail. Who wants such a gift?

I waited for my therapist to comment on the ants but she didn't. Possibly she was discreetly waiting for me to speak. I'm sorry, we need to stop here, but perhaps we can revisit this topic next time. Although the ants are probably not real, I think it would be a good idea for both of us to forget about wearing sandals until we get to the bottom of this.

FLIGHT & FILTH

Today for the first
time I saw pigeons, or any
birds for that matter, fucking; not
in flight, as I might have thought, but
in a street. The one underneath crouched
on the hard macadam while the one above
fluttered its wings, as if imagining itself in flight,
or as if desiring to meld the two desires, flying and
fucking. I stood by for the thirty seconds or so it lasted,
wondering if birds actually can and do accomplish this act
in mid-air, and if birds wonder about us: our meek obedience to
gravity, our terrestrial unions; our dense bones, useless wide blades
across the back sprouting merely the long humerus; skin unstippled,
naked even of humble pin-feathers. We consume their eggs and
flesh, whistle their calls, adorn ourselves with feathers, but no
sympathetic magic will ever lift one human body into mid-
air, let alone two together. And if birds live without
curiosity, if their knowing of this world excludes
future, doubt, choice, what ifs, if they dwell
in an unshadowed present, then I think
they may be soaring in some purer
realm even while humping
on a filth-encrusted
road.

A Dog's Tale

When the train outside the house
and the train on the screen
both whistled, the dog of the house
regarded me, forehead wrinkled, as if
to ask Is life imitating art, or vice
versa? I had no answer to give, or only
one subsumed in the murk of steam, wheels
on steel rails, and the romance
of departure.

        Then she ran to the door
when there was knocking in the movie,
and I realized this dog's ability to distinguish
fact from fiction was as tenuous
as my own.

Together we curled on the couch
to see out the film to its bitter-
sweet end. The heat of her body
and softness of her fur were as real
as real can be.

ODE TO THE DOBERMAN'S CEREBELLUM

The man in the street says
as the dog grows, you've got to monitor
the ratio between the length of the nose
and the size of the cranium; the danger
with Dobermans is that the cerebellum
will outpace its housing
and press against the bone
and that's when they'll suddenly
turn—turn on you, turn violent,
turn aside from the path of
righteousness. And if that fraught
ratio is reached, what then? Trepanning
of the skull? Anyway you've got to admire
a world in which you can simply
walk your dog and receive
a story like this one.

                    The dog
in question pushed her lengthening
muzzle against his hand, asking
to be petted.

The Unbark

I'm like a dog
who barks when the doorbell rings
on TV, or since I rarely bark,
more like the dog who doesn't bark
when the doorbell doesn't ring. It's my new
cell phone that rings, but doesn't ring—
instead it plays music, and I think
the music is playing in the movie
I'm watching, and so I don't respond
and the music doesn't sound like a dog
or a train in the distance but more like
a tango in the life I don't lead, the one
where the dog who doesn't live with me
howls to the *milongas* and once in a while
I howl too, sounding a little but not that much
like a *bandoneón* played badly
by a neophyte *acordionista*.
Without answering, without heeding,
with ears pricked up, I make my nervous
circles and lie back down, wishing
someone
would call.

Czesław Miłosz Buys Lion or Tiger Urine at the Oakland Zoo

—or so it has been reported: or rather, so goes the report
of his intent, unaccompanied by any definitive evidence
of whether he did so, or no. He loved the deer, their musky
attendance at his dwelling in exile on the western
coast of this country, in the hills above Berkeley, at the edge
of the regional park called Tilden. But he loved also his garden,
the trees, the new life that both burgeoned and was encouraged
to burgeon; and the deer loved these too, but after their fashion,
which tended toward destruction. So other than building
eight-foot-high fences to exclude the visitors, the best
modern alternative to discourage their appetite
was to spread the urine of their enemies
about the perimeter of the property.

Although I cannot say whether the intended purchase was made,
the end of the story is that on the morning when news arrived
of Miłosz's faraway death in his once homeland, deer congregated
in the small yard, more than had ever been seen there. I like
to imagine them pushing and milling, crowding, stamping, bidding
a cervine farewell to a poet and a century, creating presence
in a place of absence.

NIGHT VISITOR

The raccoon feeds itself
with clever clawed feet
from the cat's bowl on a shelf
near the foot of my bed
while my clever flawed head awakes
and my feet and hands tense,
ready for the leap
I may have to make
if its head, full of teeth,
heads in my direction
looking for more to eat.
The cat's fare and door
suit this masked visitor
who flows from perch to floor
when I stir and prepare
to deal with the intruder
to house, bedroom — even more
to that space we designate
for sleep, for love, for naked
moments between clothed,
so that finding a marauder
in this particular place
in the smallest hour of night
outrages what decorum is left
in one who rarely sleeps,
whose loving long ago ended,
whose breast is not seen
by foreign eyes unless
you count the backward glance
this beast may have cast
as it raced for the cat door.

LAND SNAIL

*"Claudius Galen, born in the second century A.D., ... described melancholic delusions —
one of his patients ... thought he was a fragile-shelled snail."*
—Andrew Solomon, The Noonday Demon

What's remarkable is that we mostly fail
to realize our inherent snailness. Fragile
or robust, we each bear a brittle shell
known to be all too susceptible
to blows, fevers, and airborne ills.
Antennae trembling, we traverse the trail
of time and space, sure of little but still
enclosed in that deceitful husk, one spill
from the end of days. And if we kill
or are killed, some call it God's will;
many commit a sin to feel a thrill.
Such revelations of the animal
within the human form may act to signal
a hunt for higher life, a call
to redemption, a deliberate swivel
of the eyestalks toward heaven; or the skill
required to pierce the protective caul
which encrypts self-knowledge, and begin to crawl
that slimy path, eternally uphill,
toward an abode beyond the frangible hull
in which we dwell, alone, beneath the veil.

NIGHTTIME ENCOUNTER

When I reached down from bed
to the water glass on the floor,
a cockroach fastened itself onto
my finger, and a cold dread swept
me, both instant repugnance
at the touch of this invertebrate
and horror at the thought
of how I might not have felt
its body against my finger
and instead would have felt
its mouth parts against my mouth,
its chitinous exoskeleton against my
oral mucosa, its fright
contacting mine,
and might even have brought
its carapace onto my tongue; and beyond
that I dare not speculate, I fear
to tread, I reject the body, the thought,
the unimaginable taste.

SMELLING THE SKUNK

makes you feel such singing aliveness, the pungency
of an odor both foul and enticing, danger
where boundaries merge, a chance
to exchange whatever thoughts are current
for sense awareness. Like pain, like self-
cutting, or similar small harms: displacing
the present rut with something compelling,
undeniable. Plus the aromatic reminder
of our former wildness, the need to discern
what is healthy for us from what is not;
the comfort of simple distinctions. The scent lingers,
evoking what has passed while insisting on now. Once known
it is not forgotten. Most hate it though a few like it,
this airborne sign of an alluring but toxic creature,
one tenuous link to the realm where good
and evil are not moral choices but questions of survival.
The merest whiff clangs alarms we can't ignore.
It makes one wonder what beauty is for.

Démons et Merveilles

BODY PARABLES

1   His knee was hurting more than usual: like a sea, with waves of pain that responded to some faraway source, dim and feeble yet strong enough to exert its influence across a vast distance. As the sky darkened at the next full moon, he applied the poultice he had made of sea salt, algae, dulse, and sea urchin eggs, soaked since the previous new moon in a tincture of blue-black ink. The pure white gauze drowned in the black, salty liquid, which ran down his shin and into his slipper. Lying on the beach with his poulticed leg propped on a Styrofoam cooler, he inspected the moon's craters and seas through binoculars.

2   She didn't remember when she first noticed her finger-nails turning pale green. They were horizontally ridged and broke easily. One hand was more affected than the other: the right, the one she used to write or draw. She pulled rusty nails from the beams of a collapsed barn, soaked them in a thickening shampoo, and buried them in the back yard by her pet turtle's grave. Two weeks later she got a new turtle and named it Nell.

3   It was because his heart had been bruised that he began eating rich foods. Pastries, ice cream, chocolate mousse — anything with plenty of lipids; the sugar didn't matter so much. In addition to the weight he knew he would gain, he thought he could add a layer of fat to his heart, a sur-rounding buffer zone which would repel any enemy fire. He had forgotten how easily a knife slices through butter.

4   The bitterness of his memories was implacable. He ate as much candy and fruit as he could, bathed in honey-scented oil, lit vanilla candles, listened to saccharine pop songs. The memories only grew more bitter in contrast to the sweetening agents he introduced. Then they suddenly crystallized, a forest of stalagmites with no path through.

5   [title? tenure] Our house is sour. The traces of our shared existence here overpower outside air. Hours, years are caught in its aura. Your part is over; ours devoured. How soon will the tawdry husk crumble? Time is more fraught than ever, more full of horror.

6   The house was sick. The house is sick. Rickety, decrepit, pitted against itself. A house divided cannot stand. Fronds of the fuchsia bush rub up against the bedroom window. Flowers of the moon stand sentinel at the corner. The scent of the Meyer lemon tree refuses to enter, even when invited. Some trees grow in houses, not necessarily glass. At the depth of the garden a tall mirror leans, reflecting on what it has seen.

7   Mites reside on our eyelashes, minute but profuse. Each blink treats multitudes to a carnival ride. Whole generations conduct their busy lives above and below the windows of the soul. Assignment to heaven, hell and purgatory may be determined by applications of cosmetics or frequency of swimming.

8   Her hair was a barometer of her mood. Shiny and full of body when she felt confident, it grew flat and dull when she was depressed, wavier at romantic times, full of static electricity when she was fearful or tense. She tried keeping it braided so it wouldn't give her away, but the braids

seemed to loosen of their own accord. The idea of cutting it felt ominous, even taboo. She took to wearing hats and acquired many. To those who knew her well, her choice of headgear was as much a giveaway of her mental state as her hair had been.

9   She was increasingly drawn to colors that hovered in between: periwinkle, teal, apricot. She stopped eating foods with simple, strong flavors and gravitated toward quince and rhubarb, mole sauce and curries. Her naturally high color faded. Even her lips paled. She seemed to waver continuously toward and away from being.

10   The pinkie toe on his left foot was so curled and twisted that it made no contact with the ground as he walked. When did that happen? he wondered. In the drawer full of old photographs, shoved into unlabeled envelopes and bearing on the reverse an identifying pencilled scrawl or nothing at all, he searched for any that displayed his naked feet in childhood. The left pinkie looked straight and narrow, but the right one was distinctly deformed.

11   She believed that certain colors had powers of attraction; others could polarize the wearer and the viewer, or even one's own personality. Early in March she began wearing yellow on Tuesdays. It could be pale as cream or verging on marigold, so long as it was yellow. By the middle of April she started having serial dreams: each night's episode continued the narrative of the previous night. After five more months she was effectively living two lives, one by day and another by night. The incident occurred when she took a nap on a warm, golden afternoon in September.

12   They tended to walk in the same order, left to right, the three of them. It just happened without volition. If they had to split up to pass an obstacle or get through a crowd or enter a doorway, they took up the same configuration afterward. Like mercury, splitting off and coming together. Like hairs that split but don't break.

13   His skin had an odd sheen, more noticeable in some lights than others. On a street after dark, when street lamps were lit, it reflected the way a sheet of glass does when you tilt it. His face always looked moist, with moisture remaining on the surface the way it does on metal. It tasted metallic too, and the aftertaste was thin and blue.

14   The eye does often feel like the I, especially when in pain. The Andalusian dog knew it and eye know it. Planetary bodies blink, are covered with darkness, send back light they have received. An orb can be the portal from inner to outer or from seeing to being seen. Please, Mr. Sandman. When Margaret's mother received a corneal implant, her friend told her the first thing she would see would be the last seen by the donor. They scoured the newspapers, the friend reading aloud any likely leads. The only recent local death was a man killed holding up a 7-11. Bull's-eye.

15   When we say thick-skinned, we're thinking of what doesn't come through from without. What about what remains within? Can it still come thinly forward? That second sort of thick skin, the one that prohibits movement from inside, seems more dammed, more damning. Our selves without outlet, our subcutaneous prison.

REMORSE HITS THE ROAD

I sent my remorse on a road trip, a wanderjahr
of self-discovery. Hitchhiking through some verdant
hills, it caught a ride with a long-distance trucker.
They ate cheeseburgers and fries at an all-night diner
and talked about failed relationships. My remorse
said it never stopped thinking about water
under the bridge, and who was the bridge
and who the water. The trucker confided
that he Googled his exes from time to time.
Together they regretted their dismal meal
as they sped down the black macadam in the black
night with their black thoughts. After what felt
like a very short time my remorse returned home,
wanderlust sated, grateful for the new sorrows
it had acquired. I thought it had gained weight,
but tactfully I said nothing.

OBLIVION, MON AMOUR

I seek you yet I know not where to look.
You flee, regarding me over your shoulder.
My efforts grow increasingly bolder.
Your maneuvers play out by the book.

Others achieve you easily, while I,
your ardent would-be lover, find only absence.
You're known to haunt some substances, like absinthe;
a fine line divides total loss from a good try.

We've had our share of one-night stands, it's true,
but what I want is something long and steady.
Your coyness leaves me cold—I feel so ready
for a folie à deux, just me and you.
I'll keep on trying till I get it right.
Just sit beside me while I dim the light.

ODE TO SORROW

You sound so ancien régime, as if your head
should have been guillotined during the Reign
of Terror; but we don't choose our names, and yours
is really quite pretty, please excuse my remarks
which I know were out of line. A pretty name, though, can hide
an ugly emotion, and love is not the only one that dare
not speak its name. So nameless shall remain
some others, but you, sorrow, feel no shame
in your title; you bravely show your tears
and downcast eyes. With sighs and murmurs
you make your presence known. I'd spurn you
if I knew how, or keep you starved and locked
in a closet. Your prettiness disguises
pain and suffering, the underbelly
of your über-cloak. And so matters must remain
until I croak.

The Mind-Body Problem Revisited

Ma Bête
The body is an animal that asserts dominion
both by punishment and by reward. My animal,
curl up with me a while; let's get better
acquainted—so many years cohabiting
and still we're strangers. Do you recall
your youth? Did my neglect surprise you?
Do you sometimes wish you could go it
alone? Neither of us has learned to accept
the ordinariness of being alive. Remember
those games we used to play, whose rules
allowed a sudden escape or a win
against the odds? Home free—that exquisite
lie. The piper must be paid. We can't live
without one another, conjoined yet not quite
twinned. Your furred existence, wild
tramplings, clear urges should not
have been declawed by my constraints.
You served me when you could. If one
of us could release the other, I'd let you go.
Forgive me my trespasses.

Ma Tête
Cher egghead, since you ask:
my youth is eternal, unaffected
by memories; each twinge
or constraint in motion
comes as a surprise which I forget
until the next assault. What you call

neglect might be better named abuse —
you used me like a mule, I was rode
hard and put up wet, you cared
for any animal or pet better
than your own! Now you feel
betrayed by what I have become.
Pose one more question: whose fault?
For that matter I've always gone it
alone: mine is the blood, salty
and raging, mine the sinew, mine
the bone. Nothing is forgiven.
I'll end our lives when the mood strikes,
with complete contempt for your loves
or likes.

PLINY: AN INTRODUCTION

1. Imagination

She was bereft. He had often seemed more like an imaginary friend than a real one. She hadn't made him up, but possibly she had enhanced the level of reality he was able to inhabit. She was bereft without there having been all that much actuality. So she brought an imaginary dog into existence: Pliny. The dog was perfect: consoling when needed, playful when wanted, never any bother, not hard to get in touch with. Always available, never annoying. Her broad skull, muscular body, trusting eyes. Unquestioned faithfulness. Walks with Pliny held so much more interest than solo outings. What attracted the dog's attention began to be noticed by the woman. Her sense of smell grew more acute, though nowhere near the subtlety of Pliny's. In the evenings they read or watched videos together, sharing the sofa. When Pliny needed to go out she didn't bark or scratch at the door; she merely gazed at the human until her message was received. The house felt harmonious.

2. Cognitive Mapping

She saw paths everywhere they weren't: across the "untamed Pacific"; creating swirls in a roof tiled in a grid; showing the way through an untracked dense forest. Leading from what had transpired to this moment. But not beyond.

3. Aggregation

She hadn't run in many years. She got a pedometer and created a log of every day's mileage. Her goal was to increase each week's total by at least ten per cent. That was somewhat of a smokescreen for the real goal, which was to run to the moon.

238,855 miles didn't seem out of the question. And anyway, she only had to do it one way.

4. This Is Not That

Something had to change. Preferably for the better. The psychic recommended moon baths and ginseng. The fortune teller predicted a crisis, followed by clarity and serenity. The psychiatrist prescribed a combination of Zoloft and cognitive behavioral therapy. Divination by entrails indicated danger at sea. The curandera suggested a sage smudge to detox the house, a sweat lodge to detox the body, and peyote to find the true way. A friend urged quick and dirty casual sex.

5. Intake

Food didn't taste right. It was metallic or it was bitter or she just wasn't hungry. Pine needles sounded good; grass smelled delicious. Additional research was called for, but she thought she might be able to adapt to a ruminant's diet.

6. Thought Process

Reading became problematic: his face, their conversations, her tears were interposed between her eyes and the page. Syllables she could easily manage, and words, but it all broke down at the level of the sentence. TV to the rescue: one series after another, even the worst dreck, like "The Bachelorette." Anything to make it that little bit harder to think.

7. *Electricity*

Where are the best places to view the aurora borealis?
Iceland. Minnesota. Anywhere north of the Arctic Circle.
Serious winter clothing would be required. Boots, a down
jacket, long underwear, mittens. Plus airfare. And lodging.
Or, she could download footage from YouTube. And watch
it in the nude. Less trouble. Still an electrical field.

8. *The Past Is Not Past*

Memory was getting patchy, reading was dicey, so she
placed a book under the pillow each night, one she had
already read. One she knew well. In the long hours before
falling asleep she would remind herself of the storyline and
the characters. In the morning she had a sensation of déjà
vu, as if she had lived the novel herself, had inhabited the
life of one or more of its characters. This feeling persisted
until at least noon, after which she felt a wrenching as of
gears as she returned to her own self.

LEAPING TREE

Thirty years ago I saw the painting
hanging in the window
of a gallery that has since folded

It was called The Suicide of the Tree
or a title very similar

From a cliff's edge a line of leafy trees
watched helpless as one of their number sprang
from the earth
and fell to its death
We didn't see the death, we saw the tree
midway down the high cliff;
we saw its companions left behind;
the back story invisible;
the moment fragmented

The descending tree's branches were lifted
slightly by momentum and uprushing wind
The speed must have been an utter shock
perhaps a pleasant sensation or at least
novel, after a lifetime of stasis

The uprooted tree continually falls yet never lands
Some of its leaves may have fluttered
upward, back up to the others

LAZARUS AND ORPHEUS IN WYOMING

The insults to the body of which the doctors spoke—
mere days post-childbirth, coma,
tissue-eating infection, and two strokes—

made resurrection seem a forlorn dream,
yet one for which he was right to pray,
since prayer and hope are what we deem

last-ditch offerings when an uncaring
or hostile universe inflicts pains
beyond all bearing.

After the devastation, the near-deaths, his will
and love dragged her back, made a place
where elusive words could find a home; and live there still.

Called back from the underworld she had found
they trod the path at a steady pace;
he knew better than to turn around.

Bidden to take up her bed and walk,
she struggles and obeys,
striding out of the fog and smoke.

The narrative reversed—
he did not turn, she reclaimed life:
which after all was not cursed.

Arisen, she casts muted light on every side,
proceeds without haste;
and he is always beside.

If light can be both wave and particle, she can shine
and reflect her former selves; be herself and not-herself in a space
of scintillating symbols, both object and sign.

Reading Catullus While Giving Blood

My hemoglobin is amazing, the nurse who shares
my birthday tells me, and I am vaguely pleased.
Without effort I have achieved bloody glory.
Many times in heart's madness she emptied her chest
...seepage of red ... What matter the numbers,
the minutes, as long as one can feed another
and still live? ... *whose existence makes me wish to live.*

The memory of love won't let you rest
and in such wakefulness
heart's hurt exhausts me always now.
Blood drains from my vein as I would wish
sorrow to drain from my heart: slowly,
steadily, to some purpose. *Delay is the waste*
of a world.... Time runs away, forgetting
what's behind it. I feel remembered
by time, held in its emptiness. My feeble
attempts to escape it go nowhere.
We all set out from home together,
but each of us takes his own path back.

Quotes from Gaius Valerius Catullus, *Complete Poetic Works*, translated
by Jacob Rabinowitz. Spring Publications, Inc. (Dallas: 1991)

Greetings from the Uncanny Valley

When that which is not human, say
a robot or a 3-D animation, approaches
the look of a human, in what is at most
an asymptotic curve, actual human beings
reach a point in their hitherto increasing
attraction where revulsion takes over. The graph
of initially mounting empathy dips
into what has been named the uncanny valley,
a locale lacking homesteads or hearths,
an uneasy state of being in which everything
gets on your last nerve. *Unheimlich,*
as Freud called it: spooky, beyond the ken,
a region we sometimes pay money to enter
but only because we know we can leave.
If the valley were physical, unhealthy miasmas
would curl from its swampy ground, the perpetually
climbing score would be written by Bernard Herrmann,
you would feel clammy and disoriented and maybe
succumb to a case of the vapors. Or you might realize
you've dwelt here all along.

I'm sure you know where this is going: We who
consider ourselves human cannot help but speculate
about everyone else; just because they creep us out
doesn't mean they're not human—although it might.
Once robots and clones grow as a population, will
we politely speak of them as differently conceived? Anyway
I just thought you'd want to read this postcard
from the slippery slope where everyone falls under suspicion
except for thee and me; and I'm not so sure about me.

AGE OF WONDER

In the faraway long ago,
much remained unknown. Not only
philosophical queries, laws
of physics, reasons to live,
and the like, but the co-star
of that film based on your favorite
childhood book, or the taxonomy
of a flower glimpsed on a walk
the day a love affair began,
and recalled with corresponding
intensity and imprecision.

All that unknowingness and some of that
curiosity has been obliterated
by the Web, replaced by interconnectedness
and a sea of linked answers. But within
those coldly informative waters swim the hideous
and entrancing creatures of the deep,
whom one may still ponder late
at night, all night, many nights, without arriving
at a single hard fact. We haven't given up
on wonder; strafed by data, it simply plunged
to the mysterious depths where its tentacles wave
gently, beckoning, promising.

VILLAINESQUE

In the current millennium
a new form of verse emerged,
based equally on the devaluing
of all the curse words thus far
devised, and on the ever-increasing
need to find someone to blame
for the mess in which the populace
found itself. The release provided
by the villainesque may have prevented
a number of homicides, while
simultaneously reducing the cost
of health care by lowering blood
pressure and the incidence of heart
attacks. Revenge being a fine
motivator, the writing of poetry
flourished, and so did publishing,
having a salubrious effect
on the domestic economy. In fact
some historians say that without
the arrival of the villainesque,
civilization as we know it
would have declined
into mere name-
calling,
aggression,
and self-
annihilation.

SPAM FROM FREUD

So many expectant days, scanning the inbox
for a message from you, the only one
who might understand me, might help,
and finally it arrives: Sender: Freud; Subject:
Your Personal Information Is Unsafe.
Yes, Herr Professor, you're right, I know that
very well and I'm on guard. Certainly what I know
is unsafe for me, or I wouldn't be in this fix; and
clearly it's unsafe for others to find out. But
should I worry about you? Surely you would safeguard
all you know about me? Or is this your subconscious
alerting me that even you are a danger? In that dark murk
we inhabit together, 50 minutes at a time, I risk many pitfalls
and lacerating edges. You seduced me, you led me down
that garden path where no flower blossoms. You promised
to stand by me and be my guide, you Virgil, me Dante.
Without your steadfast presence I would have remained
above as long as I could, on that thinning ice. So now
that we're here, my clammy palm clasped in yours,
my palpitating consciousness trying to fend off
its fears yet not get rebuked for being defended, asked
to expose its dankest corners to the healing light,
you've got to come through, fulfill my slender
trust. If I'm unsafe with you I'm better off not knowing.

I've decided to add you to my Blocked Senders List,
for after all you're only mortal, you suffer
your own psychic wounds. In parting
I suggest you seek professional help, as you're exhibiting
classic symptoms of transference. I used to think you dead,

which you may interpret as a typical twist
on the Electra complex which so fascinated you
a hundred years ago. Even the dead
can send messages, as we know;
so your missive doesn't convince me one way
or the other. In any case, Herr Doktor, we're through.
Don't email, don't call me; I'll call you.

On Watching a Documentary about Julio Cortázar

The film was in Spanish, no subtitles,
and I was following some parts better
than others, and then suddenly Cortázar
was speaking French and Spanish subtitles appeared,
and because I am more confident about reading any language
(except English) than listening to it, and because
if something is there to read, I will read it,
I continued listening to the French, which I understood
fairly well, while reading the Spanish,
and although reading is faster than speaking,
reading Spanish while translating heard French
is a slower faster, so what with the speed discrepancy
and the three languages, two not mine, I felt a peculiar
sensation as of tectonic plates grinding, which I believe
was the two lobes of my brain struggling against each other—
as they do so often in attempts to interpret others' actions
or words, not to mention my own; or in the desperate
and constant endeavor to splice meaning to the bones
and flesh of the world, for which many find subtitles in the Koran
or the Old or New Testaments or the Bhagavad Gita or drugs
or some kind of retreat within a cocoon, but I, yo, je, don't know
how to read those runes, I'm illiterate and remain
puzzled by physical ciphers besides
and feel I am slipping
plunging dizzily
into the fault
between

METEOROLOGY

My personal information
is backed up by the cloud —
and by "the cloud" I mean
not one but various: some
cumulus, some nimbus,
several cumulonimbus; and the better
aspects of me, shall I say those most
worth archiving, rare charged
filaments among the coarser stuff,
are found slowly condensing in cirrus
wisps. When I hunt for a word, shreds
of moist air mix with water
droplets; breezes riffle
more lazily than I would like
through these ethers, a few molecules
at a time. Childhood memories sometimes drift
so far above me that they become
irretrievable.

When a brainstorm is coming on
I smell ozone, pungent and fresh, as I did
once on the high desert before lightning
struck the earth and travelled up
the dog's body into my hand resting
on his head, and jolted the herd we watched
into a plunging gallop the length
of the corral. But my recollection
of that day is clouded by time,
by forgetting, and by homesickness.

Vapors of the past can crystallize,
but much remains nebulous.
Like a rose, remembrance arrives
with its disintegration prefigured. Like
a person, who knows the book's ending. Unlike
a plant or an animal, who gets to live the story
unaware of the outcome. The plots
may differ but the exit is the same, and before
reaching the legend "The End,"
anything in the world
can happen.

THE PROBLEM OF SEX IN BOOKS

I like to read how men write about sex.
For this one it's all about his sensations; he's forgotten
the existence or participation of the secondary character
he created. That one writes the woman's point of view.
Not very well, in my opinion. Another composes
a tone poem of mood and feeling. Now
we're getting somewhere. How to describe what is
beyond description? And whose every occurrence
is unique? The poets err on the side of metaphor.
Is the experience really like anything else at all?
The fiction writers pile on the graphic details,
thinking to convince by addition. If you have to ask,
I can't explain it. As for the women, fewer even go there,
and, like the men, some succumb
to focusing on a body part (not always that one)
and thereby surrender the forest
for the sake of a single tree. The tree may be lovely
but it's no glade, teased by light and shadow, interrupted
by birdsong, filled with sinuous breezes and the barely audible
sounds of a stream as it traces mossy stones,
flavored with the pungent scent released by crushed leaves,
marked by the confusion of branches, the clarity
of glimpsed sky, a place you can lose and find and lose
and find your self.

When I Was a Beauty Queen

I was dying to taste my own pillowy lips,
which looked ever ready to bestow a blow job;
I wondered if I'd be able to blow myself.
Self-tickling doesn't work but since you can excite
yourself, auto-kissing seemed dimly possible.
You can smell your own excretions but can
you taste your flesh? It's like a fish knowing
how wet the water is on a particular morning.

All those millions of fans with voracious eyes,
their clammy skins and racing pulses,
left me unstirred. Many called me icy, aloof,
as if I had any relation at all to those others,
as if we dwelt in the same universe.
What hurt was the distance between me and me,
the body I could neither escape nor possess,
the scent I couldn't perceive, the responses
I could set in motion, alone or partnered,
only by fantasizing someone else, someone
infinitely alluring, some one the only one,
the only me.

When We Were Fourteen

We were desperate
for experience, eager
to neck with almost anyone
in narrow alleys, or
semifinished basements.
Our unwieldy virginities
dragged behind us like
misshapen growths
or fatty, scaly iguana tails.
Bravado escorted us
on most of the journey,
until it burned away,
leaving exposed skin, yearning
to be stroked. But that skin
couldn't yet discern
one touch from another,
or recognize a new friend;
its nerve endings had to develop
at their own pace, which
lagged behind the mental lust
we already felt. So we faked
the passion we had only heard
about, thinking that made us
more grown up, not knowing
how much we didn't know,
what there was to learn
and the pleasure to be found
in yielding to the learning.

When I Was a Boy

I was afraid of the girls: their cliques and all
that gossiping made me sick for them all.

Their willingness to wear dresses
showed they bought into the rhetoric and all.

Worthwhile activities like climbing trees or bicycling
were severely hampered by such icky folderol.

Submitting to unfair constraints was a sign of insanity.
To those girls, my refusal was cryptic above all.

I never had an imaginary friend, only an imagined
boy self. Girls got the short end of the stick is all.

I tested my physical courage all the time,
while fearing my own destiny, private, public: all.

The stirrings of sex made me abandon boyness.
But I never betrayed the flame that flickers at all.

Heaped with protective coals, it smolders on and on.
Lisa — Jerry, your life emerges from an alembic. Fire is all.

When I Was a Martian

The women and also the men
of Ecuador, or most of them,
were shorter than I am;
that must have been part of it
but not all. My hair was dark then,
and long, but everything
about my personal style
or lack thereof
screamed *norteamericana*,
or at least Not From Here.
People stared at me on the streets. I grew uglier
and larger day by day as I ingested what tasted like
hostility or even horror. Every morning
when I passed the older gentlemen
who sat on a bench in the park,
under the palo verde tree, I said a polite
Buenos días. They looked back
but never replied.

Finally I noticed the iguanas hovering
overhead in the branches, and asked
about them. Those lizards made me human:
the men explained what they fed them,
and when, and talked about the habits
and lives of iguanas. We exchanged greetings and chitchat
each morning thereafter. My antennae shrank,
my skin color changed from blue to tan,
and I learned to breathe this rich mix
of oxygen and nitrogen. Soon
I began growing scales, but that
is another story.

When I Was Human

All that wanting
swallowed my life—
it was a boa and marmot
situation

The me that was the boa
was insatiable

Marmot-me squeaked its protest
but succumbed
over and over

Even wanting the wanting
to stop
availed not

At last
we swallowed
our own tail

WHEN I WAS SCHRÖDINGER'S CAT

The box I was in
or was not in
was not a box, but life,
and whether I was alive
or not alive was not the
question. The question
was how to get out
of the box.

FALLING UPWARD

That time I awoke   on a narrow spit of land
zipped into a sleeping bag   lying flat on my back
my eyes opened wide   and saw only night sky
no horizon: I myself   was the highest point
no frame of reference   no proprioception
vertigo overcame me   I felt I was falling
into the dense stars   (as in fact we are)
my arms flailed   clutching at the Earth

Some moments elapsed   until I oriented in space & time
It gives me pleasure to think   that for those instants
my relation to the universe was true   unfiltered: direct experience
unmediated by knowledge   In the universe I inhabit now
memory is more authentic   than current reality

but there are still stars

Penumbra is set in Diotima, designed by Gudrun Zapf von Hesse in 1948. The titling font, Alcuin, was designed by von Hesse in 1986. She based it on the letterforms of the Carolingian minuscule. The cover and section title font is Cézanne, based on the artist's handwriting.

Notes

Re "The Voyage":
  In Oliver Goldsmith's "An Elegy on the Death of a Mad Dog" (1766), dog bites man and

> The man recovered of the bite,
> The dog it was that died.

  Samuel Johnson, quoted by Boswell: "Sir, a woman's preaching is like a dog's walking on his hind legs. It is not done well; but you are surprised to find it done at all."

"Démons et Merveilles" is the title of a song featured in Marcel Carné's 1942 film *Les Visiteurs du Soir*. The words are by Jacques Prévert, with music by Maurice Thiriet.

Acknowledgments

Grateful acknowledgment is made to the editors of the following publications, where some of the poems in this book first appeared.

Five Fingers Review: "Navigation"
Aftermaths/Figments, a double chapbook (Etherdome): "My Cousin and I Chat about Old Times," "On Watching a Documentary about Julio Cortázar," "Eating Chocolate Cake with the Lights Off," and "Body Parables" (in slightly different form)
Visions International: "The Problem of Sex in Books"
Caesura: "Reading Catullus While Giving Blood"
Nostos (three volumes): "The Space Between," "Lazarus and Orpheus in Wyoming," "Remorse Hits the Road," "When I Was a Beauty Queen," "When I Was a Boy," "When I Was Human," "Arc," and "Coffee Cake"

Lisa Rappoport is a poet, book designer, letterpress printer and book artist, creating limited edition artist's books and poetry broadsides under the imprint Littoral Press. Her book *The Short Goodbye* received the Alastair Johnston Fine Press Award and was runner-up in the Carl Hertzog Award for Excellence in Book Design. Her work is in national and international collections and has been included in such surveys as *500 Handmade Books, Volumes I & II* (Lark Books) and *1000 Artists' Books* (Quarry Books). She is also the editor of *Letters from Wupatki* (University of Arizona Press). Her website is littoralpress.com.